MINDFUL MANTRAS

I WILL BE OKAY!

My name is Max, and all day long,
I know I'll be okay.

By Laurie Wright
Illustrations by Ana Santos

Some days I feel grumpy and I don't want to be at school. Will I be okay?

I can talk to
other people at school,

I can run and play
and have fun at recess,

I can learn new things!

I will be okay.

When I have a fight with a friend I feel really sad.
Will I be okay?

I can play
with other friends,

I can tell an adult
about my feelings,

I can say "I'm sorry"
to my friend.

I will be okay.

I feel confused sometimes when I have to do hard things. Will I be okay?

I can ask for help,

I can tell myself
I CAN DO THIS, and
try again,

I can tell myself
that it's okay to feel
confused sometimes!

I will be okay.

I feel overwhelmed when too many things are happening around me. Will I be okay?

I can go somewhere
more quiet,

I can close my eyes
and think of something
I love to do,

I can find my friend to
get a GREAT BIG HUG!

I will be okay.

I feel anxious when I meet someone new. Will I be okay?

I can tell someone
how I feel,

I can smile and wave
instead of saying hello,

I can understand that
it's okay to feel this way.

I will be okay.

I get nervous when there's a lightning storm!
Will I be okay?

I can close all the
windows and curtains,

I can cuddle under the
covers with someone,

I put on earphones so
I don't hear the noise.

I will be okay.

I get scared in the dark at night. Will I be okay?

I can get into bed
with someone else,

I can turn on
my flashlight,

I can hug my blankie
and stuffy SO hard.

I will be okay.

I feel worried when my parents go out without me. Will I be okay?

I can try to have fun
with the babysitter,

I can paint them
a picture,

I can make them a
present and put it on
their bed!

I will be okay.

I feel discouraged when I try so hard and things still don't turn out right. Will I be okay?

I can blow bubbles
to calm down,

I can go for a walk and
enjoy being outside,

I can take a break
and then try again.

I will be okay.

I don't know how I feel when I don't know HOW I feel! Will I be okay?

I can try to eat something, that helps a lot.

I can talk to someone about how I don't know HOW I feel!

I can do yoga to relax so I can think more clearly.

I will be okay.

Sometimes I feel confused, scared, anxious, angry, sad, grumpy, confused, worried, overwhelmed and sometimes I just don't know how I feel!

But I know I will be okay!

My name is _____

...and I will be okay!

Dear Readers,

After reading this book you've realized that you will be okay, even when the dog eats your favorite shoe, or when your brother breaks your Lego, or when you have to go to bed. By often saying to yourself "I will be okay!", it will soon become an automatic thought.

Now, I have a question for you. How do you handle it when someone else gets to open presents, and you don't? How do you handle it when you see someone in a costume? How do you handle it when you have to try new food at someone else's house? If your answer was 'I FREAK out!' to any of those questions, you might want to read the book, "I Can Handle Special Occasions" in the Mindful Mantra series.

(here is a little secret: adults have trouble handling special occasions sometimes too!)

Get it now, and get a handle on special occasions!

~Laurie

Laurie Wright

Laurie Wright is a speaker, author, and educator who is passionate about helping children increase their positive self-talk and improve their mental health. Laurie speaks to parents, teachers, has given a TEDx talk, created resources and has written 3 books, all to further the cause of improving the self-esteem of our children. Laurie is a huge advocate for children's mental health and works every day to improve the way we interact with kids, and to help them learn to handle all of their emotions!

Ana Santos

Ana is a creative and innate illustrator and she feels very comfortable and inspired by all the challenges and areas that incorporate illustration and design. Graduated in graphic design, she dicovered her vocation for Arts as a child. Ana has already several years of experience in graphic design and illustration and she has already illustrated several edited children's books for people and publishers around the world! Ana is an artist attentive to new technologies working on many internet platforms as a freelancer.

Made in the USA
San Bernardino, CA
25 June 2018